FOLENS One-a-Week

Spelling Tests BOOK 3

Rita Ray

Editor: Michael Spilling
Layout artist: Patricia Hollingsworth
Cover illustration: Patricia Murray – Graham-Cameron Illustrations
Illustrations: Cathy Gilligan

Reprinted 1998.

British Library Cataloguing in Publication Data. A catalogue record for this book is available from the British Library.

First published 1997 by Folens Limited, Dunstable and Dublin.
Folens Limited, Albert House, Apex Business Centre, Boscombe Road, Dunstable, LU5 4RL, England.

ISBN 1 85276 445-7

Printed in Singapore by Craft Print.

Introduction

One-a-Week Spelling Tests provide a graded set of practice exercises and tests to build up spelling skills. The words have been selected from research into words most used by children at particular stages.

The words are arranged in small groups, which can be focused upon and tested periodically. The units contain key sight words and words with common spelling patterns. In books 1–4, words with similar spelling patterns are presented together and tested in separate sentences. In books 5 and 6, similar spelling patterns are spread throughout the books so that they can be tested in the context of whole passages. This provides a suitable preparation for the format of national tests.

The sentences used in books 1–4 are of necessity simple, and set the target words in contexts familiar to most children. They should be able to focus on the target word without the distraction of an over-stimulating context; for this reason the sentences are low-key in content.

The tests should be dictated to the children. Each child should have a copy of the test and add the missing word as the sentences are read aloud to them.

The practice pages help children to learn the spellings through a variety of activities that are directed towards meaningful repetition of the words. The importance of writing for reinforcing spelling patterns is recognised.

Consistent practice is essential in building up familiarity with frequently occurring patterns and key words. This series will help ensure that children attain competence in spelling at each stage.

Exercise 1

- Complete these sentences with words from the list.

To look after is to take ________ of.

The opposite of old is ________ .

________ grows on some animals.

________ means not strong.

A ________ is a person who looks after sick people.

You keep money in a ________ .

________ means no good.

A kind person is usually ________ .

________ means handy and helpful.

Untidy work is ________ work.

- Finish the words.

n __ __ __ e　　c __ __ __　　u __ __ f __ __

c __ r __ __ __ __ __　　p __ __ s e　　w __ __ __

__ e __ __ l __　　__ o __ __ g　　u __ __ __ __ __ s

- Look  cover  write 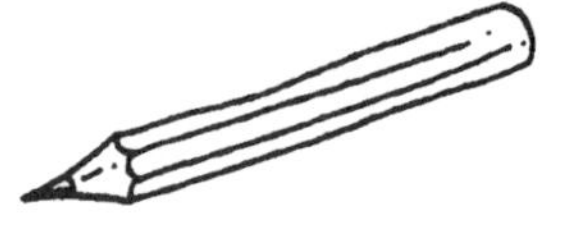

young ________　purse ________　useful ________　care ________

Test 1

- As each line is read to you, write the words in the spaces.

1. Take ________ of your new coat.
2. If you are ________ you will make a mistake.
3. My new pencils are very ________.
4. The broken bike is ________.
5. The boy was ________ with the injured bird.
6. A ________ dog is called a puppy.
7. Cats have soft ________.
8. There is a ________ in the medical centre.
9. Put the change in your ________.
10. The little dog was too ________ to jump.

✓ or ✗	
1.	
2.	
3.	
4.	
5.	
6.	
7.	
8.	
9.	
10.	

- Copy two sentences in your best handwriting.

____

____

____

____

SCORE

Practise these:

Exercise 2

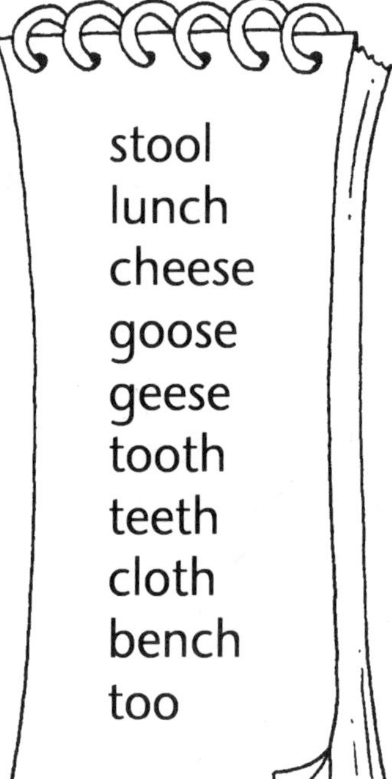

- Look at the words on the list. Finish the words.

te ___ ___ ___   ___ o ___ ___ e

l ___ ___ ___ h   g ___ ___ s ___

c ___ ___ ___ s ___   ___ ___ n ___ h

___ ___ ___ ___ l   c ___ ___ ___ ___

___ o ___ ___ h   ___ ___ ___

- Sort the words and write them on the chart. **Tooth** and **teeth** have been done for you.

ending in **th**	ending in **ch**	words with **ee**	words with **oo**
tooth teeth		teeth	tooth

- Look  cover  write 

stool ____________ cheese ____________ bench ____________

Test 2

- As each line is read to you, write the words in the spaces.

1. I like to sit on a high ________.
2. We had fish fingers for ________ today.
3. Put ________ spread on the sandwich.
4. The ________ laid a golden egg.
5. Ten ________ live in the farmyard.
6. The baby has a new ________.
7. The dentist is coming to look at our ______.
8. Wipe the juice up with a ________.
9. There is a ________ to sit on in the park.
10. Claire put ______ much salt in her soup.

✓ or ✗	
1.	
2.	
3.	
4.	
5.	
6.	
7.	
8.	
9.	
10.	

- Copy two sentences in your best handwriting.

____

____

____

____

____

____

____

SCORE

Practise these:

Exercise 3

change
changed
break
broke
broken
brighter
brightest
miner
safer
deeper

- Look at the words. Put them into three families in the boxes below.

change break brighter
broken brightest broke changed

- Fill in the missing words.

bright brighter brightest

________ safer ___________

________ __________ deepest

- A miner can be a coal miner or a gold miner. Draw a miner in the box.

- Look  cover  write 

change ____________ broken ____________ brightest ____________

Test 3

- As each line is read to you, write the words in the spaces.

1. Please ________ into your PE kit.
2. The teacher ________ the date on the board.
3. Try not to ________ the plate.
4. John ________ his leg on the ski slope.
5. Sharpen the ________ pencil.
6. The sun seems ________ in summer.
7. Which star looks ________?
8. The coal ________ has a lamp on his helmet.
9. It's ________ to cross the road at a crossing.
10. The big lake is ________ than the small one.

- Copy two sentences in your best handwriting.

____

____

____

____

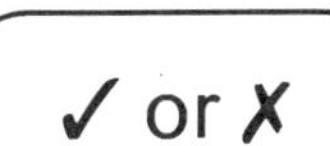

✓ or ✗	
1.	
2.	
3.	
4.	
5.	
6.	
7.	
8.	
9.	
10.	

SCORE

Practise these:

Exercise 4

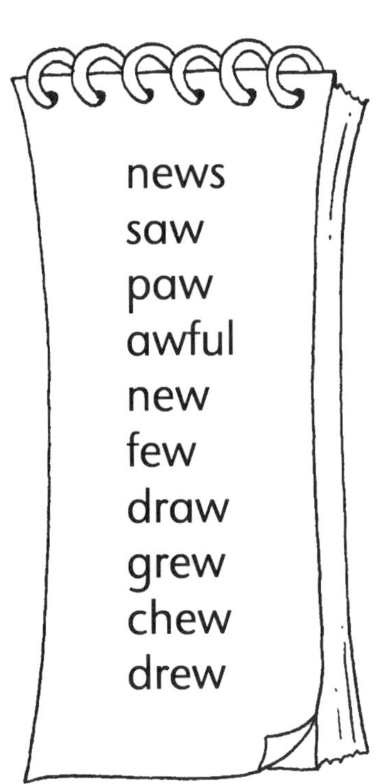

- Look at the words on the list.
- Put the words in the right spaces.
- Write the words into the crossword.
  1D = 1 down **1A** = 1 across

1. Don't let the dog __________ (1D) your shoes.
2. My cat hurt her __________ (5D).
3. Have you heard the __________ (2A)? School is closed today.
4. I can __________ (6A) pictures.
5. I __________ (6D) a picture of my friend.
6. The plant __________ (7A) bigger.
7. Jill looked out and __________ (3D) the __________ (4A) weather. She got her umbrella.

- Look  cover  write 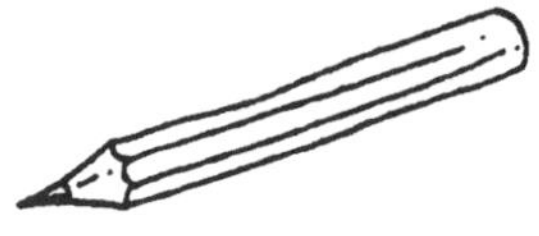

few __________ new __________ awful __________ saw __________

Test 4

- As each line is read to you, write the words in the spaces.

1. I watched the ________ on television.
2. Bill ________ a plane in the sky.
3. The dog put his ________ in the paint.
4. Jane's green socks looked ________ .
5. I need ________ trainers.
6. Put a ________ sweets in your pockets.
7. Can you ________ cars?
8. My sunflower ______ as high as the house.
9. You must not ________ gum in class.
10. The artist ________ a picture of me.

✓ or ✗	
1.	
2.	
3.	
4.	
5.	
6.	
7.	
8.	
9.	
10.	

- Copy two sentences in your best handwriting.

____

____

____

____

SCORE

Practise these:

Exercise 5

hiding
smiling
shining
hoping
chief
thief
clever
nearly
should
would

- Finish the patterns.

ing ing ____________________

ie ie ____________________

ou ou ____________________

- Add **-ing** to these words.
  Remember to take off the **e.**

hide ____________

shine ____________

hope ____________

smile ____________

- Read the sentences. Circle the words that are in the word list.

The clever thief nearly bumped into the chief guard.
"You should not be here!" said the guard.
"I would like to go home," said the thief.
"I'm not so clever after all."

- Look 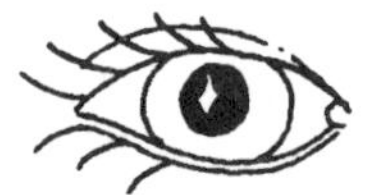 cover  write 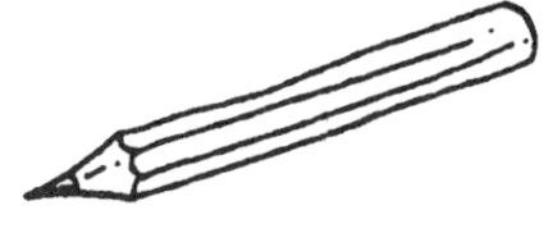

hoping ____________ should ____________ thief ____________

Test 5

- As each line is read to you, write the words in the spaces.

1. Jan was ________ in a tree.
2. Everyone was ________ in the photo.
3. The light was ________ through the window.
4. Danny was ________ to buy some skates.
5. The ________ constable gave the policeman a medal.
6. A ________ stole the videos.
7. The ________ dog rescued the boy from the river.
8. We ________ won the netball match.
9. You ________ study quietly.
10. I ________ like you to come to my party.

- Copy two sentences in your best handwriting.

____

____

____

____

____

____

____

✓ or ✗	
1.	
2.	
3.	
4.	
5.	
6.	
7.	
8.	
9.	
10.	

SCORE

Practise these:

Exercise 6

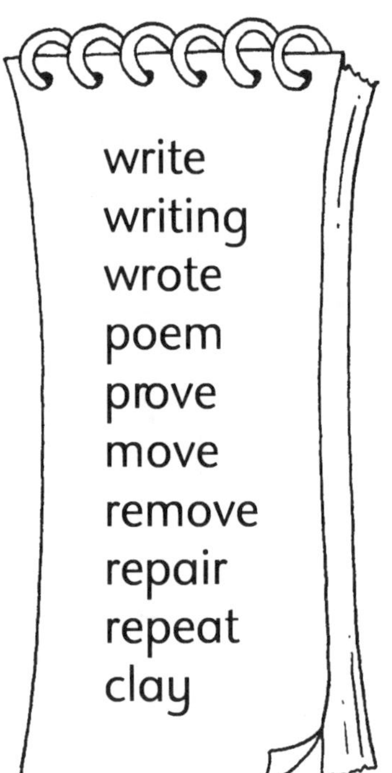

- Look at the list.
  Write the words beginning with **wr**.

  ____

  Write the words beginning with **re**.

  ____

- Put the words in the right spaces.

  write **poem** **writing** **wrote**

Every morning we have maths, reading and ________ .
I like to ________ poetry. Yesterday I ________ a
________ about spring.

- Write the words ending in **ove**.

  ____

- Write the word that rhymes with play. ________

- Look 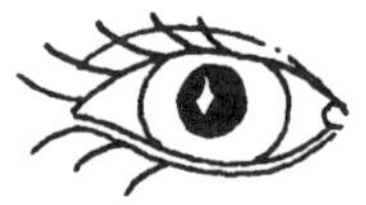 cover  write 

prove ________ repeat ________ wrote ________

Test 6

- As each line is read to you, write the words in the spaces.

1. We can ________ to our friend in America.
2. This pen will help you to do your best ________.
3. The head teacher ______ a notice in the hall.
4. I want to learn that funny ________.
5. Can you ________ that you were not here?
6. You can ________ nearer to the television.
7. Please ________ your muddy shoes.
8. The plumber can ________ the taps.
9. If you _______ the words you will learn them.
10. The potter makes things with ________.

✓ or ✗	
1.	
2.	
3.	
4.	
5.	
6.	
7.	
8.	
9.	
10.	

- Copy two sentences in your best handwriting.

____

____

____

____

____

____

____

SCORE

Practise these:

Exercise 7

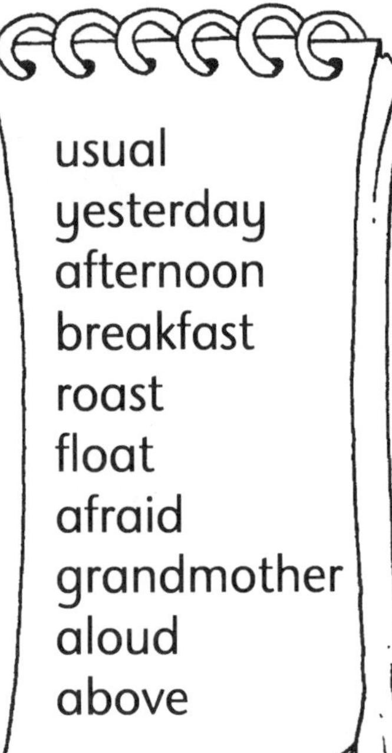

- Read the passage.
- Underline all the words from the list.

Yesterday I went to school with my grandmother as usual. I had toast for breakfast and I took roast chicken crisps for lunch.

In the afternoon we saw a strange shape float above us in the playground. We were all afraid.

"What is it?" whispered the teacher. Then she said aloud, "Go and phone the police!"

- List the words that you have underlined.

____________ ____________

____________ ____________

____________ ____________

____________ ____________

____________ ____________

- What do you think the shape was?
- Draw it in the box.

- Look cover write

breakfast ____________ usual ____________ roast ____________

Test 7

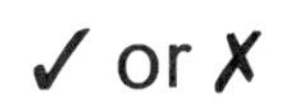

- As each line is read to you, write the words in the spaces.

1. Come to school as ________ next Monday.
2. The doctor came __________ .
3. We have silent reading every __________ .
4. Some people eat cereal for __________ .
5. My brother eats nothing but _____ potatoes.
6. Wood can usually _______ better than metal.
7. The cat was ________ of the dog.
8. Red Riding Hood's ____________ lived in a cottage.
9. We have to read ________ in the hall today.
10. The star is shining ________ the roof.

- Copy two sentences in your best handwriting.

✓ or ✗	
1.	
2.	
3.	
4.	
5.	
6.	
7.	
8.	
9.	
10.	

SCORE

Practise these:

Exercise 8

branch
branches
classes
glasses
together
towards
forward
order
border
worth

- Finish the word squares.

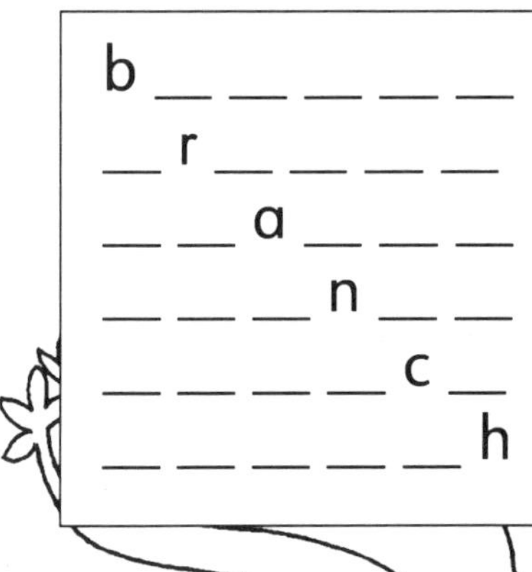

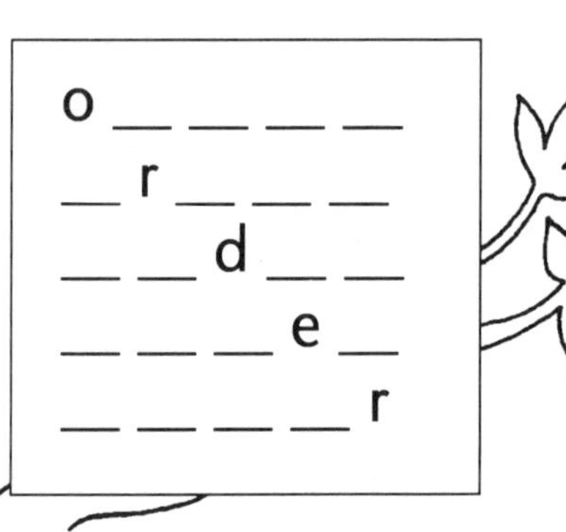

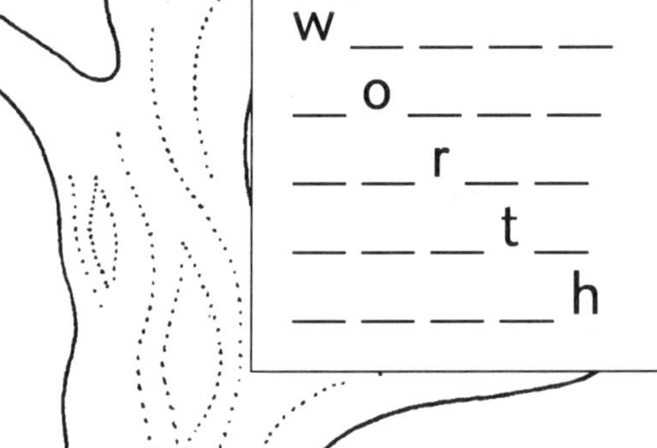

- Write the rhyming words.

order ________________

classes ________________

- Write the words that contain **ch**.

____

- Write the words beginning with **to** and **for**.

____

- Write the words with **ss**.

____

- Look 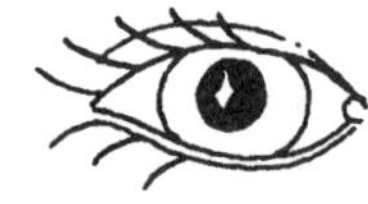 cover  write 

branches __________ towards __________ glasses __________

Test 8

- As each line is read to you, write the words in the spaces.

1. The apple hung from the ________.
2. The kite was stuck in the ________ of a tree.
3. There are eight ________ in our school.
4. I drank three ________ of water.
5. Let's sing this song ________.
6. The ball bounced ________ the goal.
7. Take four steps ________ when I tell you.
8. Please ________ a pizza for me.
9. Draw a pattern round the ________.
10. This chocolate is not ________ twenty pence.

✓ or ✗	
1.	
2.	
3.	
4.	
5.	
6.	
7.	
8.	
9.	
10.	

- Copy two sentences in your best handwriting.

____

____

____

____

____

____

____

SCORE

Practise these:

Exercise 9

thirteen
thirty
fourteen
forty
price
twice
since
fence
hurry
chance

- Write the words for the numbers.

13	30	14
________	________	________

40
____

- Read the sentences.
- Write out the words in boxes.

1. Can you jump over the high fence twice?

________ ________

2. I have not seen Gemma since last year.

____

3. You must hurry or you'll miss your chance of a free bike.

________ ________

4. The price of this comic is forty pence.

________ ________

- Look  cover  write 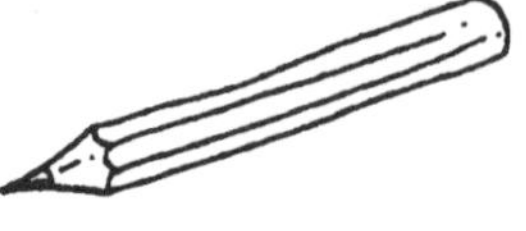

hurry ________ since ________ fourteen ________

Test 9

- As each line is read to you, write the words in the spaces.

1. There are ________ days before my birthday.
2. There are ________ days in September.
3. A fortnight has ________ days.
4. I'm reading 'Ali Baba and the ______ thieves'.
5. What is the ________ of this toy?
6. We've seen this film ________.
7. Gran has been here ________ Tuesday.
8. We'll put a ________ up to keep the dog in.
9. Please ________ to the bus stop.
10. This is your last ________ to buy books.

✓ or ✗	
1.	
2.	
3.	
4.	
5.	
6.	
7.	
8.	
9.	
10.	

- Copy two sentences in your best handwriting.

____

____

____

____

SCORE

Practise these:

Exercise 10

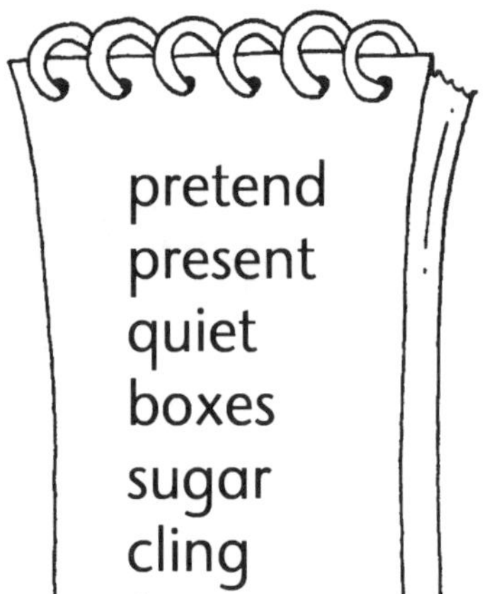

- Join the two parts of each word.

- Write the words beginning with **pre**.

- Write the words with **ing** in them.

- Write the words for numbers.

- Look  cover  write 

sugar ____________ quiet ____________ boxes ____________

Test 10

- As each line is read to you, write the words in the spaces.

1. Let's ________ to be pop stars.
2. We are buying our teacher a ________.
3. It's very ________ in the middle of the night.
4. How many ________ of crayons do we need?
5. There's a lot of ________ in that pudding.
6. David had to ________ to the side of the boat.
7. Don't leave ________ marks on the glass.
8. My brother is ________ years old.
9. There are ________ eggs in a dozen.
10. The baby ________ her milk all over my work.

✓ or ✗	
1.	
2.	
3.	
4.	
5.	
6.	
7.	
8.	
9.	
10.	

- Copy two sentences in your best handwriting.

____

____

____

____

____

____

____

SCORE

Practise these:

Exercise 11

hundred
space
spider
soap
soak
earth
daisies
invite
friend
tenth

- These words are mixed up. Write out the words correctly.

oaks ______________
epacs ______________
saidsie ______________
dripes ______________
vintie ______________
nudherd ______________
heart ______________
apos ______________
dreifn ______________
hentt ______________

- Find the words in this puzzle. Colour them yellow.

k	r	t	s	o	a	p	m	e	a	r	t	h
x	s	p	a	c	e	g	j	s	o	a	k	f
r	t	h	u	n	d	r	e	d	z	c	v	l
m	d	k	d	a	i	s	i	e	s	p	d	w
s	p	i	d	e	r	v	b	t	e	n	t	h
x	z	r	w	i	n	v	i	t	e	j	t	d
p	f	r	i	e	n	d	c	z	f	w	q	r

- Look  cover  write 

daisies ______________ friend ______________ earth ______________

Test 11

- As each line is read to you, write the words in the spaces.

1. I can jump one ________ times.
2. There is enough _______ in your exercise book.
3. Meera would like a pet ________.
4. It's fun to make ________ bubbles.
5. You must ______ the muddy socks in water.
6. The ________ goes round the sun.
7. There are ________ growing all over the grass.
8. I hope you ________ me to the party.
9. I cannot sit next to my ________ on the bus.
10. It will be Ben's ________ birthday soon.

- Copy two sentences in your best handwriting.

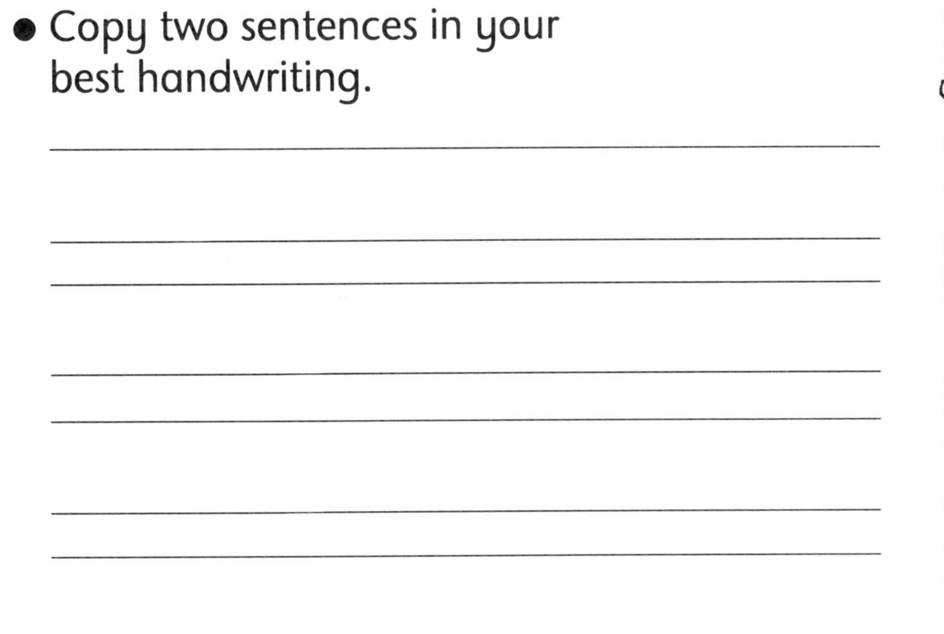

✓ or ✗	
1.	
2.	
3.	
4.	
5.	
6.	
7.	
8.	
9.	
10.	

SCORE

Practise these:

Exercise 12

half
halves
themselves
thieves
wheel
between
fifteen
knife
knives
knock

- Look at the list.
  Find words with **ee**.
  Find words with **kn**.
  Put them in the right boxes.

ee	kn

- Fill in the missing words.

	halves
thief	
knife	

- Read the sentences. Put the words in the right spaces.

between **thieves** **half** **fifteen** **knock**

1. Cut the pie in ________. We can share it ________ us.
2. The ________ were soon arrested.
3. You have to ______ hard at the door of number ________.

- Look  cover  write 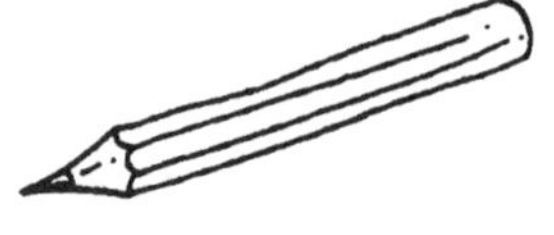

themselves __________ wheel __________ knives __________

Test 12

- As each line is read to you, write the words in the spaces.

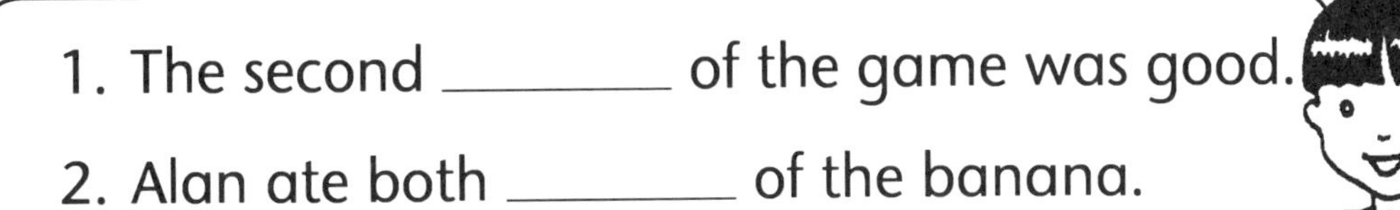

1. The second ________ of the game was good.
2. Alan ate both ________ of the banana.
3. The children helped ________ to the biscuits.
4. The ________ took the cakes from the stall.
5. We need another ________ for our model car.
6. Stand ________ the goalposts.
7. Geeta swam ________ lengths of the pool.
8. Each place needs a ________ and fork.
9. Those ________ are for cutting bread.
10. Always ________ before you go into the room.

- Copy two sentences in your best handwriting.

✓ or ✗	
1.	
2.	
3.	
4.	
5.	
6.	
7.	
8.	
9.	
10.	

SCORE

Practise these:

Exercise 13

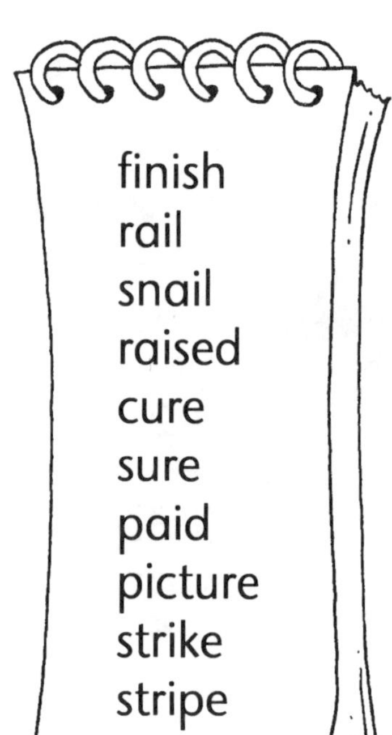

- Look at the list.
- Write the words with **ai** in this box.
- Write the words with **ure** in this box.
- Write the words with **str** in this box.

There is one word left on the list.

- Write it here. ___________

- Finish the words.

s _ _ _ l

s _ _ _ k _

s _ _ _

p _ _ d

_ ai _ _ _

r _ _ _

_ _ r _

_ i _ _ _ _ _ _

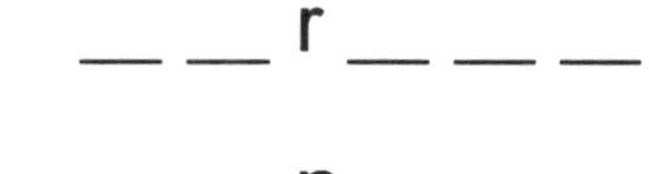

_ _ r _ _ _

_ _ n _ _ _

- Finish the pattern.

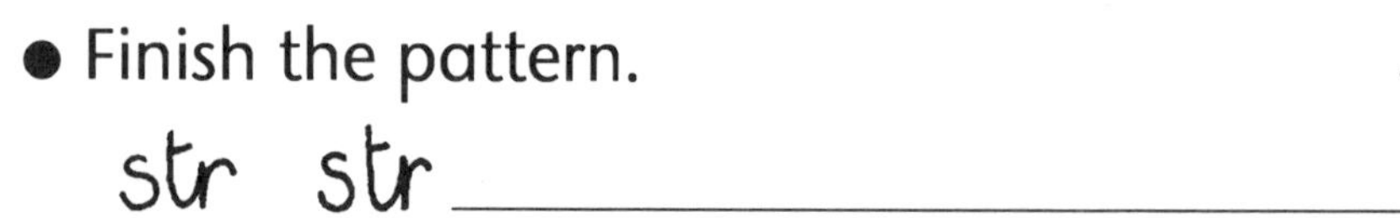

- Look  cover  write 

stripe ___________ picture ___________ sure ___________

Test 13

- As each line is read to you, write the words in the spaces.

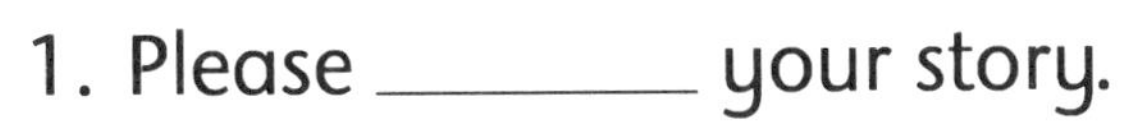

1. Please ________ your story.
2. Hang your towel on the towel ________.
3. The ________ has a shell on its back.
4. The shopkeeper ________ the price of ice-cream.
5. This medicine will ________ your cough.
6. I'm ________ I gave you the fifty pence I owed.
7. He ________ for the bike out of his savings.
8. There is a ________ of our school in the paper.
9. The clock will ________ every hour.
10. The guard has a red ________ on his sleeve.

- Copy two sentences in your best handwriting.

____

____

____

____

____

____

____

✓ or ✗	
1.	
2.	
3.	
4.	
5.	
6.	
7.	
8.	
9.	
10.	

SCORE

Practise these:

Exercise 14

nothing
running
better
animal
follow
borrow
narrow
someone
something
sometimes

- Match the two parts of the words.
  Write the words on the lines.

noth	one	________
run	low	________
fol	ing	________
bor	mal	________
some	ter	________
ani	mes	________
somet	row	________
narr	ning	________
bet	hing	________
someti	ow	________

- Put the words in the right spaces.

follow **better** **animal**

1. The ________ started running. The girl wanted to ________ it, but the animal was a ________ runner than the girl.

borrow **nothing**

2. Last week I had ________ to read so I went to ________ a book from the library.

- Look  cover  write 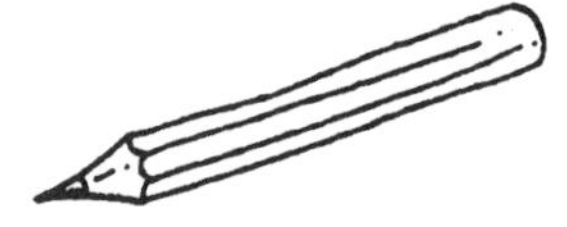

something ________ narrow ________ sometimes ________

Test 14

- As each line is read to you, write the words in the spaces.

1. There is ________ left in the packet.
2. Sara was ________ round the track.
3. This story is ________ than the last one.
4. A cheetah is a spotted ________.
5. You can ________ Ahmed in the line.
6. We can ________ two books every week.
7. The path through the woods is very ________.
8. I think ________ was looking for you.
9. Would you like ________ to eat?
10. We like to go to a disco ________.

- Copy two sentences in your best handwriting.

✓ or ✗	
1.	
2.	
3.	
4.	
5.	
6.	
7.	
8.	
9.	
10.	

Practise these:

Exercise 15

power
shower
towel
strange
large
danger
hungry
shadow
touch
answer

- Finish the word squares.

- Read the sentences.
- Circle the words from the word list.
- Write them on the lines.

1. A large bird flew over the house. It was a strange bird.
   It looked hungry. Were we in danger?

   __________ __________ __________ __________

2. We like our new power shower.

   __________ __________

3. I like to touch this soft towel.

   __________ __________

4. Can you answer this question?
   Is your shadow longer in the afternoon?

   __________ __________

- Look  cover  write 

strange __________ shadow __________ answer __________

Test 15

- As each line is read to you, write the words in the spaces.

1. The engine has a lot of ________.
2. Nigel got caught in a ________ of rain.
3. You need a ________ to dry your hair.
4. I like stories about ________ planets.
5. The café sells ________ cups of coffee.
6. The bridge is in ________ of falling down.
7. The ________ dog took the pie.
8. We made ________ puppets for a play.
9. Don't ________ the hot pan.
10. Please ________ the door for me.

✓ or ✗	
1.	
2.	
3.	
4.	
5.	
6.	
7.	
8.	
9.	
10.	

- Copy two sentences in your best handwriting.

____

____

____

____

____

SCORE

Practise these:

Exercise 16

- roll
- rolled
- form
- thorn
- gather
- path
- yellow
- pillow
- understand
- understood

● Look at the list.
Finish these words.

_ _ ll   th _ _ _

_ _ ll _ _   _ _ th _ _

y _ ll _ _   _ _ th

_ ill _ _   _ _ _ _ m

u _ _ _ _ _ _ o _ _

_ _ _ _ _ s _ _ _ _

● Find eight of the words in this puzzle. Colour them yellow.

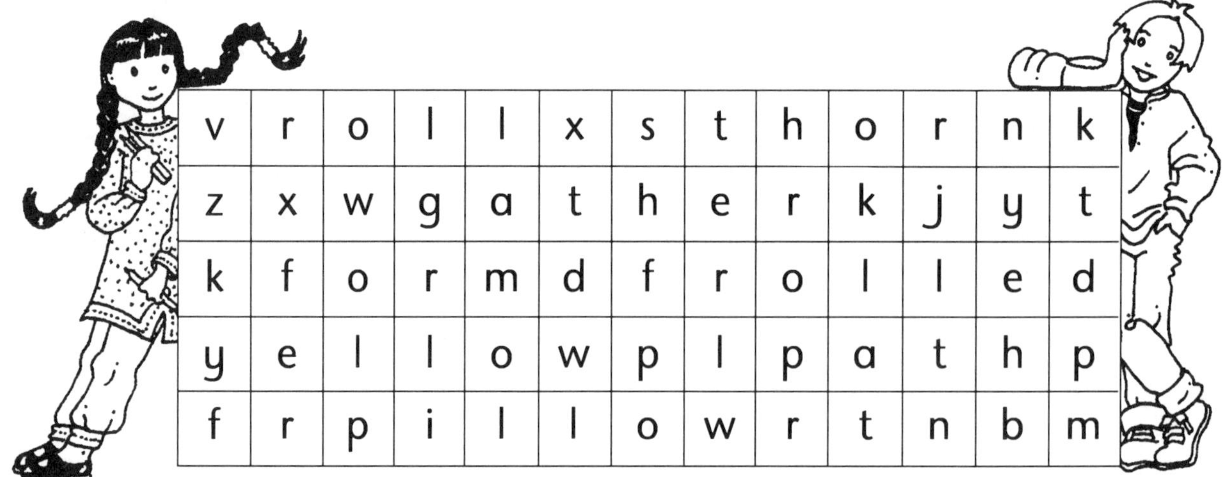

v	r	o	l	l	x	s	t	h	o	r	n	k
z	x	w	g	a	t	h	e	r	k	j	y	t
k	f	o	r	m	d	f	r	o	l	l	e	d
y	e	l	l	o	w	p	l	p	a	t	h	p
f	r	p	i	l	l	o	w	r	t	n	b	m

● Look  cover  write 

understand ____________ gather ____________ pillow ____________

Test 16

- As each line is read to you, write the words in the spaces.

1. Gran made a lovely chocolate ________.
2. Phil laughed as he ________ down the hill.
3. Fill in this ________ to get the free offer.
4. The lion had a ________ in its paw.
5. You need to ________ lots of blackberries to make jam.
6. Draw a house with a red ______ in front of it.
7. There are ________ balloons tied to the fence.
8. We need an extra ________ for this bed.
9. Do you all ____________ this test?
10. Tara ____________ the computer game.

- Copy two sentences in your best handwriting.

✓ or ✗	
1.	
2.	
3.	
4.	
5.	
6.	
7.	
8.	
9.	
10.	

Practise these:

Exercise 17

travel
begin
began
crown
crowd
growl
owl
bringing
handle
candle

- Finish writing the words.

- Look at the words on the list.
- Find the right words to fill the spaces.

1. Are you ______________ your brother to the party?
2. Tigers can __________ .
3. An __________ is a bird.
4. You can __________ a long way in a car.

- Fit the words into the grid.

- Look  cover  write 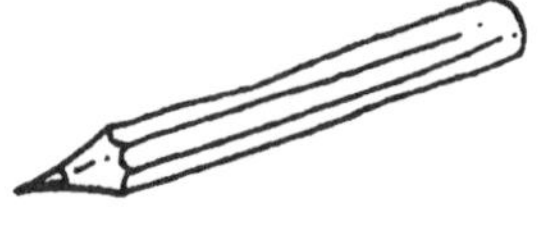

begin __________ growl __________ candle __________

Test 17

- As each line is read to you, write the words in the spaces.

1. We booked a holiday at the ________ agent's.
2. We shall ________ eating now.
3. The film ________ at eight o'clock.
4. Draw a ________ on the queen's head.
5. There was a big ________ at the game.
6. The tiger will ________ at you.
7. The ________ hunts at night.
8. The van is ________ me a parcel.
9. The ________ of my suitcase has broken.
10. We had to light a ________ during a power cut.

✓ or ✗	
1.	
2.	
3.	
4.	
5.	
6.	
7.	
8.	
9.	
10.	

- Copy two sentences in your best handwriting.

____

____

____

____

SCORE

Practise these:

Exercise 18

anybody
nobody
Thursday
Friday
happen
person
bear
wear
carpet
angry

- Fill in the missing segments.
- Write the words on the lines.

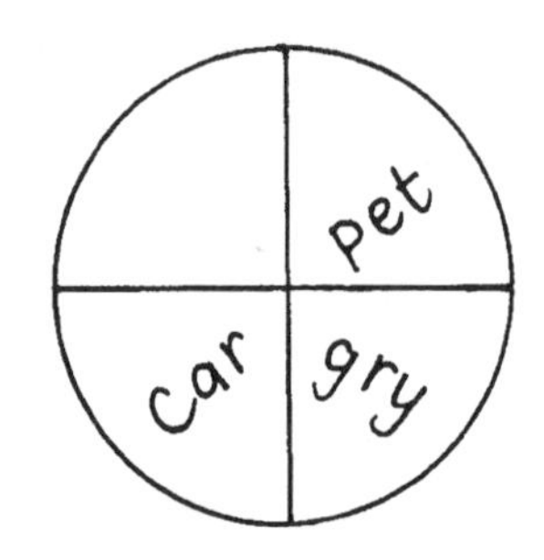

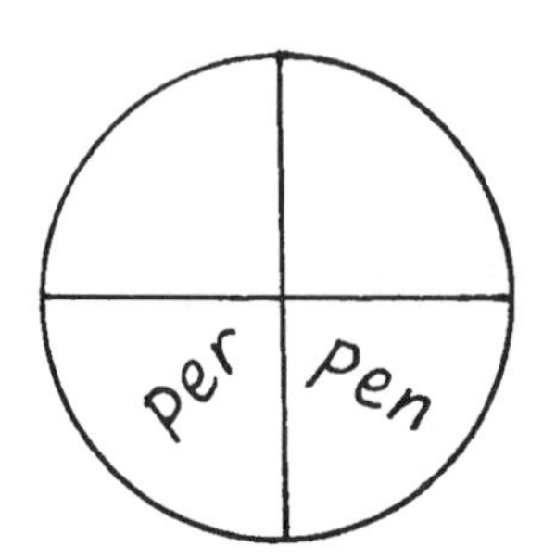

____________ ____________

____________ ____________

- Write the rhyming word.

bear __________

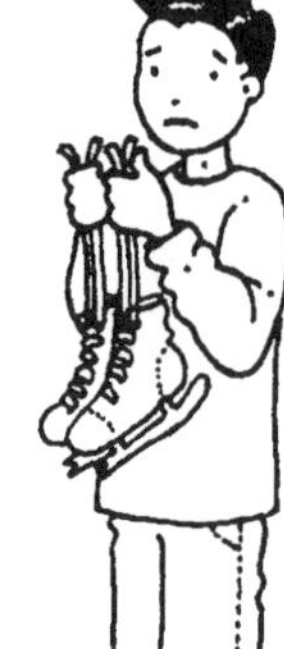

- Put the words in the right spaces.

Thursday anybody Friday nobody angry

1. Did ________ call when I was out?
   No, ________ called.
2. Jenny was ________ when Carl broke her skates.
3. Monday, Tuesday, Wednesday, ________ , ________ .

- Look  cover  write 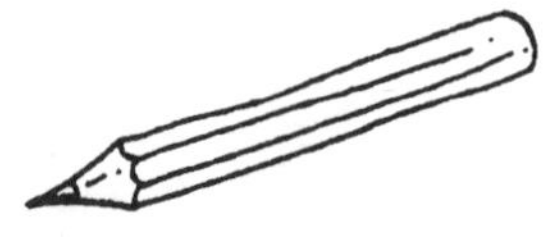

person ________ happen ________ Friday ________

Test 18

- As each line is read to you, write the words in the spaces.

1. Has ________ seen my scarf?
2. There is ________ in the classroom.
3. Grant is coming to visit on ________.
4. We have pizza every ________.
5. What will ________ if I press the button?
6. A thief is a bad ________.
7. I can't ________ it when you scrape the board.
8. My sister likes to ________ my clothes.
9. We sit on the ________ to talk.
10. Jack made the giant ________ in the story.

✓ or ✗	
1.	
2.	
3.	
4.	
5.	
6.	
7.	
8.	
9.	
10.	

- Copy two sentences in your best handwriting.

____

____

____

____

____

____

____

SCORE

Practise these:

Exercise 19

build
building
bottle
kettle
rattle
scrape
frame
shy
butterfly
spy

- Read the sentences and fill in the missing words.
- Write the words into the crossword.

DOWN

1. Polly put the ________ on.
2. A castle is a big ____________ .
3. Please ________ the old paint off.
4. A red admiral is a kind of ____________ .

ACCROSS

4. I need a big ________ of milk.
5. The wind makes the door ____________ .
6. The photo is in a gold ____________ .
7. This word rhymes with spy. ____________

- Look 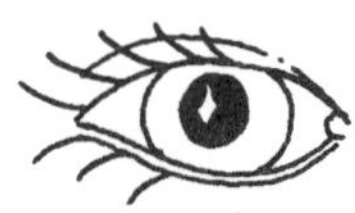 cover  write 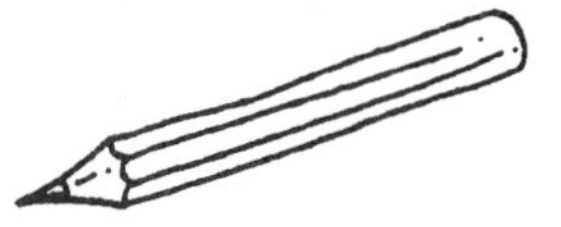

build ________ spy ________ scrape ________ rattle ________

Test 19

- As each line is read to you, write the words in the spaces.

1. You can ________ a model with this kit.
2. That ________ has ten floors.
3. Pour the juice into a ________.
4. The ________ is boiling.
5. The baby is shaking her ________.
6. It's hard to ________ burnt pans.
7. Put that photo of Dad in a ________.
8. The ______ girl did not want to be in the play.
9. The caterpillar changed into a red ________.
10. The ________ hid behind a tree.

✓ or ✗	
1.	
2.	
3.	
4.	
5.	
6.	
7.	
8.	
9.	
10.	

- Copy two sentences in your best handwriting.

____

____

____

____

____

____

____

Practise these:

Exercise 20

easy
easier
easily
heavy
heavier
question
tired
matter
swimming
slipped

- Fill in the missing words.

easy	
	heavier

- Finish the patterns.

tt ______________________________

mm ______________________________

- Read the sentences.
  Circle the words from the list.
- Write them in the box.

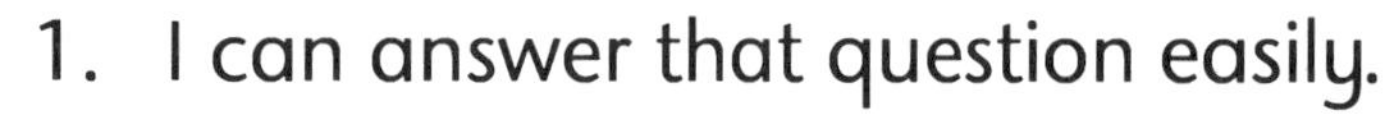

1. I can answer that question easily.
2. Tom slipped at the swimming pool.
3. It doesn't matter how tired you are.

- Look 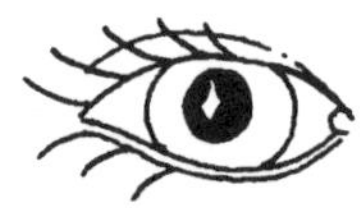 cover  write 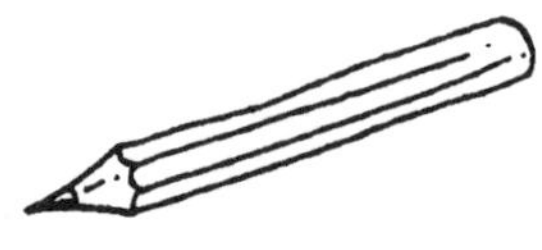

heavy __________ tired __________ question __________

Test 20

- As each line is read to you, write the words in the spaces.

1. Making a cake is ________.
2. Knitting is ________ than sewing.
3. I can throw the ball into the net ________.
4. My lunch box is ________.
5. My cat is ________ than your dog.
6. When I'm not sure I ask a ________.
7. Molly was ________ as she had stayed up late.
8. It doesn't ________ how long you stay.
9. The ________ pool is cold today.
10. The skater ________ on the ice.

- Copy two sentences in your best handwriting.

✓ or ✗	
1.	
2.	
3.	
4.	
5.	
6.	
7.	
8.	
9.	
10.	

SCORE

Practise these:

Exercise 21

- Look at the words on the list.
- Here are two pairs of words.
  Find other pairs.

		They both have:
stream	straw	str
music	refused	us

- Read the sentences. Write out the words in boxes.

1. There was a [princess] who had to spin [straw] into gold.

   ____________ ____________

2. The [donkey] [refused] to cross the [stream].

   ____________ ____________ ____________

3. The [monkey] could play [music] on a whistle.

   ____________ ____________

- Look  cover  write 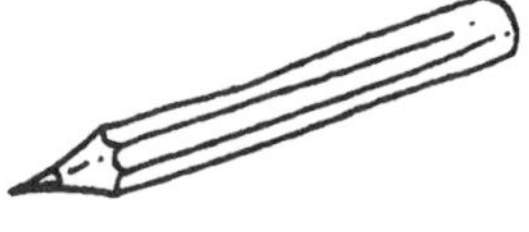

tied ____________ prince ____________ straw ____________

Test 21

- As each line is read to you, write the words in the spaces.

1. The ________ ran down the hillside.
2. The rabbits have ________ in their hutch.
3. A king and queen's son is called a ________.
4. There is usually a ________ in fairy tales.
5. Our school ________ is blue.
6. Your shoelace is not ______ properly.
7. I rode a ________ on the beach.
8. The ________ enjoys playing tricks.
9. The ________ teacher says we must practise.
10. The boy ________ to give the bully some money.

- Copy two sentences in your best handwriting.

✓ or ✗	
1.	
2.	
3.	
4.	
5.	
6.	
7.	
8.	
9.	
10.	

SCORE

Practise these:

Exercise 22

brain
chest
heart
cheeks
unpack
untie
undo
dislike
dishonest
unfair

- Label the picture.

- Write the opposite of these words.

fair ____________

like ____________

honest ____________

- Finish the patterns.

dis dis ________________________________

un un ________________________________

- Read the sentences.
- Put the words in the right spaces.

untie **unfair** **unpack**

1. Our holiday is over. We can ________ our case.
2. I can't ________ the knot in this string.
3. I always get the blame. It's ________ .

- Look cover write

brain ________ dishonest ________ heart ________

Test 22

- As each line is read to you, write the words in the spaces.

1. The scientist used his ________.
2. The ball hit the player on the ______.
3. The swimmer's ________ was beating fast.
4. The jogger had red ________.
5. Help me to ________ the bags.
6. I like to ________ the string on parcels.
7. Jake can't ________ his coat yet.
8. We ________ the food in that café.
9. The __________ girl tricked the shopkeeper.
10. It's ________ to let Ryan do all the tidying up.

- Copy two sentences in your best handwriting.

✓ or ✗	
1.	
2.	
3.	
4.	
5.	
6.	
7.	
8.	
9.	
10.	

SCORE

Practise these:

How well did I do?

Shade in your test scores on this graph.

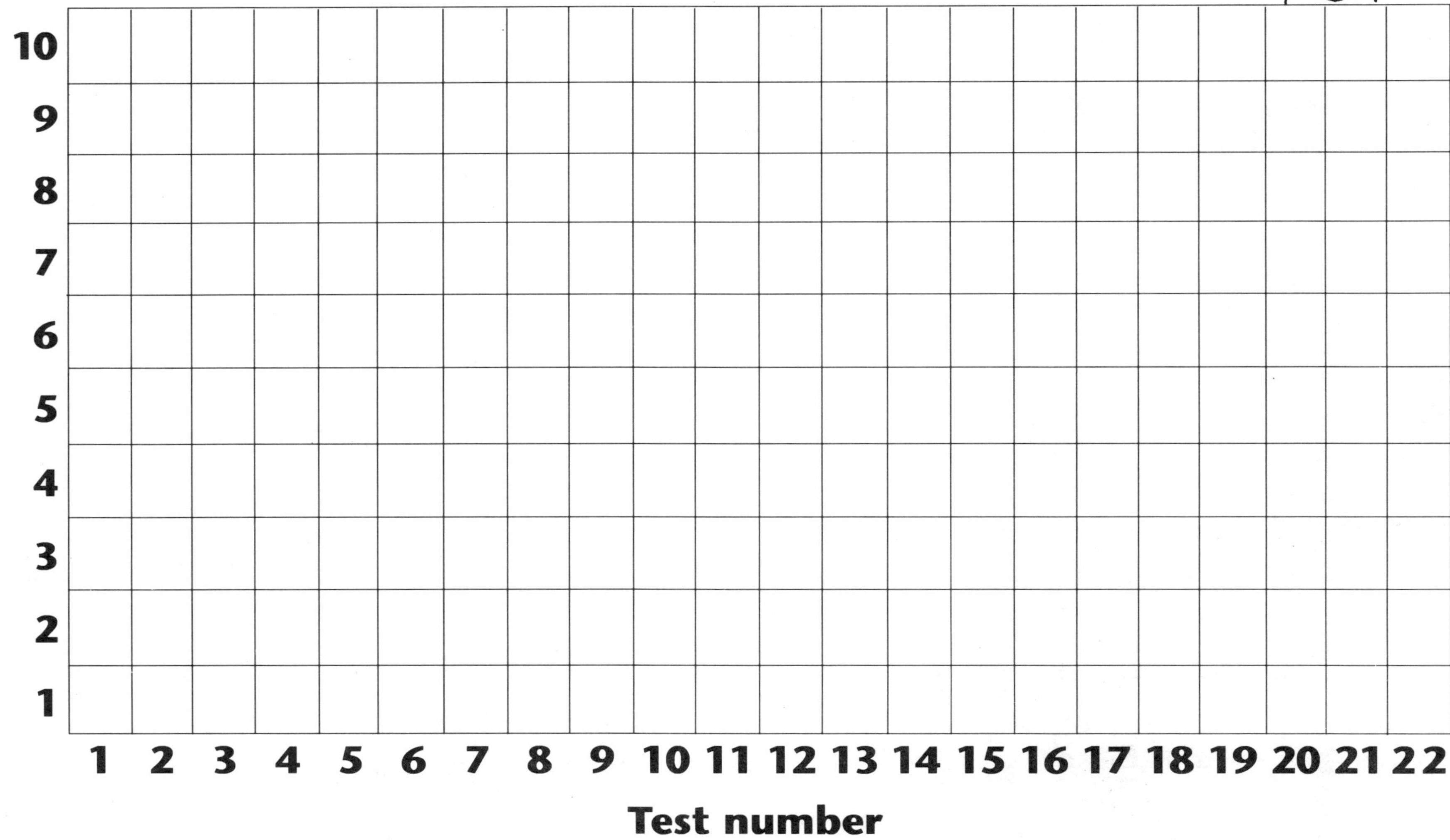